SCHOOL-LIVE! DESIGN WORKS

SCHOOL-LIVE! CHARACTER DESIGNS ①

SCHOOL
LIVE!
VOLUME
1

⊘ YUKI TAKEYA (SCHOOL UNIFORM, FRONT)

ART BY SADORU CHIBA
STORY BY NORIMITSU KAIHOU (NITROPLUS)
VOLUME 1

SCHOOL-LIVE!

SUU
(ZZZ)

SUU

AHEM.

HELLO?

KA
(CLACK)

KA

SUU

SUU

TAKEYA-SAN?

YUKI TAKEYA-SAN?

KON
(THUNK)

YEAAAH?

PACHI
(BLINK)

HMM?

Yuki...
you've been
sleeping for
too long...
you should
wake up...

ZZZ.

IT'S NOT MEGU-NEE.

IT'S SAKURA-SENSEI.

OKAY! SO, WHAT IS IT?

OH, THAT'S RIGHT!

SHOULDN'T YOU BE AT THE CLUB?

HA (GASP)

I REALLY LIKE SCHOOL THESE DAYS.

I'LL BE THERE LATER. SAY HELLO TO EVERYONE FOR ME.

OKAY!

OKAY, THEN! I'M OFF! WHAT ABOUT YOU, MEGU-NEE?

IT SHOULDN'T BE "THAT'S RIGHT" ANYMORE.

TA TA TA

GAKU (TWITCH)

WAY TO GO, MEGU-NEE. THERE'S NO POINT TO THE SCHOOL LIVING CLUB IF YOU GO HOME.

YEAH! OH, WHATCHA EATING?

PORI (CRUNCH)

YEAH, BUT MEGU-NEE REMINDED ME.

THAT WAS REALLY CLOSE!

I ALMOST FORGOT ABOUT CLUB AND WENT HOME BY ACCIDENT.

TEE HEE!

CAN: HARDTACK

PAKU (CRUNCH)

HARDTACK REALLY HAS THIS SURVIVALIST FEEL, DOESN'T IT?

IT'S KINDA EXCITING.

SURE!

HARD-TACK.

WANT SOME?

SOUNDS GOOD.

GACHA (CLATTER)

LET'S GO CHECK IT OUT TOO.

THE PRESIDENT'S UP ON THE ROOF HELPING THE GARDENING CLUB.

KYORO (GLANCE)

KYORO

WHERE'S RII-SAN?

PORI PORI

EVERYONE IN THE GARDENING CLUB, WE'RE HERE TO HELP!

BISHI (FWIP)

SURE! LEAVE IT ALL TO THE SCHOOL LIVING CLUB!

THANKS, AS USUAL. CAN WE LEAVE THE REST TO YOU?

YEAH, WE'RE HERE TO HELP.

OKAY, THEN. THANKS!

PON (PAT)

ピン
PIN (THWIP)

BAD!

WAH!

S-SORRY.

HUH? REALLY?

SHE SAID SHE ALMOST WENT HOME AFTER CLASS TODAY.

OH! NO TELLING!

LISTEN, RII-SAN. YOU KNOW WHAT SHE DID—

ビッ
BI! (POINT)

SCHOOL LIVING CLUB RULE NUMBER ONE!

YEAH.

KOKU KOKU (NOD)

IT'S LIKE A TRAINING CAMP, SO EVERYONE HAS TO BE HERE.

AND, UM, DEVELOP A MORE A... AUTONOMOUS ATTITUDE—

...ALLOWS US TO BECOME MORE FAMILIAR WITH VARIOUS AREAS OF THE SCHOOL THAT YOU CAN'T FIND IN CLASS BY STAYING IN THE SCHOOL ITSELF.

TO UTILIZE ALL THE FACILITIES OF THE SCHOOL AND STAY OVERNIGHT!

バーン
BAAN (TADAA)

OH!

RULE NUMBER ONE. THE SCHOOL LIVING CLUB...

HEY, KURUMI-CHAN, LOOK AT THAT! THEY'RE WAVING AT ME.

HIRA (WAVE)

HIRA

HEEEY!

WHOA, THE BASEBALL TEAM'S REALLY PRACTICING HARD.

REALLY?

HIRA

HIRA

STOP GOOFING...

...OFF!

THE BACK OF THE BLADE IS.

キラーン

KIRAAN (GLINT)

WHOA! USING THE SHOVEL'S NOT FAIR!

BIKU (FLINCH)

GA (WHOOSH)

GA (GRAB)

NOW YOU'VE DONE IT!

GEEZ! IN THAT CASE...

...TAKE THAT!

BASHA (SPLASH)

WHOA!

BA (FWIP)

UGH.

I'M ALL WET...

GUSSHORI (SOAKED)

WINNER.
↓

YEAH!

KYAA!

WAAH!

YOU TWO...

...WHAT ABOUT HELPING OUT?

OKAY!

YOU'RE TOTALLY SOAKED. GO GET CHANGED BEFORE YOU CATCH A COLD.

HEY! YOU'RE THE ONE WHO STARTED IT!

RII-SAN, KURUMI-CHAN'S SO MEAN!

TA (TROT) た た た た っ

HEBUSHI (ACHOO)

FUKI (WIPE)

......

......

WILL SHE BE OKAY BY HER-SELF?

GACHA (KACHAK)

SFX: SA (FWISH) SA

SHE'S JUST SO RECKLESS...

YOU WORRY TOO MUCH. BESIDES, MEGU-NEE'S THERE TOO.

WHAT IS IT? DID YOU FORGET SOMETHING?

WAH!

KURIHI

GII (CREAK)

HYOKO (PEEK)

OH, NO, THAT'S NOT IT.

I WAS JUST THINKING THAT I REALLY LIKE ALL OF YOU.

UMMM.

...BUT IT'S NOT LIKE I FORGOT ABOUT YOU GUYS OR ANYTHING.

WELL...

I FORGOT WE WERE STAYING OVER AND ALMOST WENT HOME...

MOJI (FIDGET)

MOJI

WHAT'S THAT ALL ABOUT?

OKAY, SEE YOU!

WHOA! IT'S REALLY COLD! SOMEONE LEFT THE WINDOW WIDE OPEN.

HYUU (WHOOSH)

BATAN (THUNK)

GARA (RATTLE)

GARA

CAN: HARDTACK

SCHOOL-LIVE!

CHIRA
(GLANCE)

ちら
ち
ら

MMM...

I DON'T
HATE
RUNNING.

けっ？
HFF...

HFF...？

けっ？
HFF...
？

BUT I
HAD AN
ULTERIOR
MOTIVE FOR
JOINING
THE CLUB.

I WAS
CHASING
AFTER
SOME-
ONE.

AND IT
WASN'T
LIKE I
WAS TEAM
MANAGER
MATERIAL.

HFF...
は
ぁ

HFF...
は
ぁ

Chapter 2

Memories

MM...

HAA.

BOOO
(DAZED)

SUU
SUU
(ZZZ)

PORI
(SKRITCH)
PORI

WHOOOOOOA!

LET'S EAT!

ALL RIGHT! LET'S EAT!

THAT'S RIGHT.

CURRY!!

DEDEEEN (TADAAA)

HUH? WE'RE A SPORTS TEAM?

IT'S FINE! I'M ON A SPORTS TEAM!

KURUMI-CHAN, YOU'RE GONNA GET FAT.

MOGU. (MUNCH)

BAN (THUD)

SO FAST!

THAT WAS REALLY GOOD! ARE THERE SECONDS?

FUU (CHAA)

OH, WATERING THE PLANTS IS PRETTY TIRING, ISN'T IT?

WE'RE TECHNICALLY A CULTURAL CLUB, BUT WE DO A LOT OF PHYSICAL LABOR, SO IT MIGHT BE LIKE A SPORTS TEAM.

KURUMI, RULE NUMBER TWO OF THE SCHOOL LIVING CLUB!

IT'S NOT ODD JO—

I KNOW, RIGHT? IT'S ALL ODD JOBS!

MU > CHMPH

TECHNICALLY I'M THE FACULTY ADVISOR, AND YET...

MUU

GOOD. NO CALLING IT ODD JOBS.

GOT IT, PRESI-DENT!

UMM, BECAUSE THE SCHOOL LIVING CLUB USES THE SCHOOL FACILITIES, WE MUST ALWAYS REPAY THAT DEBT.

RULE NUMBER TWO.

. . .

SUU
(SIGH)

PATAN
(SHUT)

OKAY...

LET'S
GO.

KON KON (KNOCK)
KON
コン フン
コン

LOOKS GOOD.

ZUUUUUN (GLOOOOOM)
ズ
ウ
ウ
ウ
ウ
ツ

WHOA!

ぬっ
NU
(LOOM)

HUP.

グ
GU
(GRAB)

BOOK: MODERN LITERATURE

UMM... LIKE THIS?

UHHH...

KARI (SKRITCH)

OH, OKAY!

GATA (CLATTER)

BOARD: SHOWERS (OCCASIONAL RAIN)

ジョオオオオオ
JOOOOO (SPLASH)

ゴシ
GOSHI

ゴシ
GOSHI (SCRUB)

YOU WORRY TOO MUCH.

IT'S DANGEROUS TO DO IT BY YOURSELF.

THERE WAS JUST ONE IN A GOOD POSITION.

YOU DID IT AGAIN? YOU ONLY HAD TO CHECK, YOU KNOW.

YEAH, YEAH.

THAT'S BECAUSE I'M THE CLUB PRESIDENT!

AHEM!

URO

URO (SHAMBLE)

URO

URO

REMEMBER? YUKI WAS SAYING THAT'S THE BASEBALL TEAM HAVING THEIR MORNING PRACTICE.

WHAT'S WRONG?

SHE DID SAY THAT.

I WONDER.

I'M WONDERING IF THERE'S ANYONE ON THE TRACK TOO.

BAG: FLOUR

PASAA
(FSSHH)

IT'S OKO-
NOMIYAKI.
LET'S HAVE
IT FOR
DINNER.

I'M
BACK!

WHAT'S
THAT?
CREPES?

HYOKO
(PEEK)

YAAAAY!
I LOVE
OKONO-
MIYAKI!

はぁあ
PAAAAA
(SHIIIINE)

あぁ

JUU
(SIZZLE)

YOU'RE QUITE LATE. WHERE'S SENSEI?

SHAKA
(FWIP)

SHAKA
(FWIP)

SPAM

...YOU'RE HOPELESS.

MUUU
(CHMPH)

YOU KNOW...IS MATH REALLY EVER GONNA BE USEFUL? THEY SAY IT'S FOR THE FUTURE, BUT I JUST DON'T SEE IT...

WE WERE DOING EXTRA LESSONS TOGETHER.

POSU
(THUNK)

RRRRRRRRRRRRRRRRR
(RUMBLING)

YEAH, YEAH.

Aww.

THEN SHOULD WE DO SOME MATH TOGETHER?

AWWW.

YOU TOO, KURUMI.

47

...OH YEAH.

LET'S ALL GRADUATE TOGETHER.

YOU'RE RIGHT! LET'S DO IT!

OKAY, FINE.

OKAAAY! IT'S ALL DOOONE!

TON (THUNK)

LET'S EAT!

HUH
...?

GOKI
(CRACK)

GOKI

SEN-
PAI?

DON
(THUD)

DON

GARI
(SCRATCH)
GARI

GATA

GATA

GATA
(RATTLE)

YURA
(SWAY)

RII-SAN,
WHAT
ARE YOU
TALKING
ABOUT?

HE'S...

GARI
(SCRATCH)
GARI

NO!
LOOK
AT HIM,
KURUMI.

DON
(THUD)

DON

GATA

GATA

GRAAAH!

GATA

KUWA
(LOOM)

WAH!?

!?

GASP!

GUU
(ZZZZ)
GUU

HFF...

HFF...
HFF...

HFF...
HFF...
HFF...
HFF...
HFF...

SO
(SLIDE)

...GOOD
NIGHT.

SCHOOL-LIVE!

BOOK: 10/4: SOLAR POWER (RAIN), PACKAGED RICE, PACKAGED CURRY, FLOUR, VITAMINS, UMAKABO, CHOCOLATE, UNIFORMS, HARDTACK 10/5: SOLAR POWER (CLOUDY) [LEFT PAGE] ONIONS HAVE SPROUTED. BRINGING THEM!!

AN ACCOUNT BOOK IS REALLY RELIABLE.

WHEN YOU FILL IT OUT, YOU CAN SEE WHAT'S COMING IN THE NEXT WEEK!

WHEN WE STARTED THIS CLUB, WE DIDN'T EVEN KNOW WHAT TOMORROW WOULD BRING. WE STILL DON'T KNOW WHAT WILL HAPPEN NEXT MONTH.

WE DON'T HAVE ENOUGH POWER.

MUU CHMM
むぅ....

I WONDER WHAT WE'LL BE DOING NEXT YEAR.

OH, WE'VE HAD A LOT OF RAIN, HAVEN'T WE?

WE'RE RUNNING LOW ON GOODS TOO. WE SHOULD PROBABLY GO GET SOME SOON.

GOT IT.

ガラ!!
GARA (SLIDE)

ばーーーん
BAAAN (TADAAAA)

ATTENTION, SCHOOL LIVING CLUB!

HMM?

WHAT IS IT?

59

HUH? NO? IT'S FEAR AND EXCITEMENT HERE IN SCHOOL IN THE MIDDLE OF THE NIGHT!

LET'S DO A TEST OF COURAGE. A TEST OF COURAGE!

HUH?

OF ALL YOUR SUDDEN IDEAS...

DAN
(THUNK)

OH, BUT IT'S A GOOD IDEA.

YOU LITTLE...

GIRI
(GRIND)

IT'S OKAY. GHOSTS ARE NOTHING IF YOU TRAIN TOGETHER WITH ME!

NO WAY!

OH, KURUMI-CHAN? DON'T TELL ME YOU'RE SCARED OF GHOSTS!

GIRI

GIRI

RIGHT?

HEH HEH...

...

GOT IT.

COULD YOU GO TELL MEGU-NEE ABOUT IT?

OKAY. I'LL HELP.

NOW THAT THAT'S DECIDED, WE NEED TO GET READY.

PATA
はた

PATA (PATTER)
ぱた

ABOUT YUKI-CHAN? WE'LL BE FINE IF WE'RE CAREFUL.

IF YOU SAY SO...

PATAN (SHUT)
ぱたん

ARE YOU SURE?

BUT THIS IS SCHOOL. THERE WON'T BE ANYTHING.

AREN'T YOU SCARED, YUKI-CHAN?

AT LEAST BE ON YOUR GUARD A BIT!

HMM. I GUESS RUNNING INTO A REAL-LIFE GHOST WOULD BE SCARY.

TEKU (TROT)

TEKU

TEKU

UGH...

BOSO (MUMBLE)

THERE ISN'T ANYONE IN SCHOOL AT THIS HOUR.

YES.

ドォ...

PITA (STOP)

SO, HOW ARE WE SPLITTING UP?

YES, YES.

Megu-nee, you have to be quiet!

ボソ BOSO (WHISPER)

ボソ BOSO

A TEST OF COURAGE IS ALL WELL AND GOOD, BUT DON'T BE RECKLESS.

HMM...

YES, LET'S DO THAT.

にこ NIKO (SMILE)

YAAY!

ぎゅ〜〜 GYUUU (SQUEEZE)

ちら… CHIRA (GLANCE)

S-SINCE WE'RE ALL HERE, CAN'T WE JUST GO ALL TOGETHER?

もじ MOJI (FIDGET)

もじ MOJI

...DON'T CALL OUT AND JUST COME BACK TO THIS STAIRCASE. OKAY?

YEAH.

EVERYONE GRAB SOMETHING AS PROOF THAT YOU MADE IT. AND IF YOU GET SEPARATED...

FIRST UP IS THE SCHOOL STORE. THEN THE LIBRARY.

UMMM... FIRST WE HAVE TO—

THEN ALL FOUR OF US WILL GO TOGETHER. DO TRY NOT TO GET SEPARATED!

ADVISOR.

...

SHOBOON (GLOOM)
しょぼーん

...

MEGU-NEE, HURRY UP!

SUTA (STEP)
スタ

SUTA
スタ

LET'S GO.

HEN, 'RYONE...

SIGN: SCHOOL STORE

UMM, PROOF THAT WE CAME, RIGHT?

RIGHT.

THERE... AREN'T ANY GHOSTS.

DON'T LET YOUR GUARD DOWN.

TAG: UNIFORM

ガサッ

GASA (RUSTLE)

SIGN: SHAMPOO

GOSO (RUMMAGE)

CHARIN (JINGLE)

WE CAN TAKE ANY- THING?

OF COURSE. WE'LL LEAVE MONEY FOR IT.

MONEY: 5,000 YEN

BAG: SCALLOP CHIPS MENTAI FLAVOR

AND UMA- KABO!

AND CHIPS!

CHOCO- LATE!

PA

PA

PA (FWIP?)

BAG: SOUMEN

YAAAY!

TA (TROT)

OH.

THEN NEXT UP IS THE LIBRARY.

HUP.

SIGN: LIBRARY

GARA
(SLIDE)

I-IT'S REALLY DARK. I WONDER IF THE LIGHTS WORK.

BUT THEN THAT WOULDN'T BE A TEST OF COURAGE. OH, WATCH YOUR STEP.

OKAY.

PARI (CRUNCH)

OH, YOU GO ON AHEAD. I'M GOING TO LOOK IN HERE.

WHAT KIND OF BOOKS ARE YOU GETTING, RII-SAN?

TEXTBOOKS AND WORK-BOOKS...

YOU REALLY LIKE STUDYING, DON'T YOU?

UGH... ⸨GULP⸩

BOOK: MATH

SASAA ⸨FWISH⸩

I-I'M GONNA GO FIND SOME BOOKS TOO!

AHHH.

AH, YUKI-CHAN!

UFU FU FU...

NO, THESE ARE FOR YOU. YOU SAID THAT THERE WERE THINGS YOU DIDN'T UNDERSTAND.

YOU SHOULDN'T BE RUNNING.

OH, MEGU-NEE.

THERE YOU ARE.

GOSO (RUMMAGE)

BOOKS: TIME / MEAT-EATING MARY / OLD MAN MAGICA / B CHANNEL / EIKEN!

I'M SORRY! ...OH?

HUH ...?

SASA (FWISH)

WH-WHO'S THAT?

MOGO (MMPH)

SHUSH!

......!

SUUU (SHAMBLE)

KYORO
(GLANCE)
キョロ

KYORO
キョロ

STAY RIGHT
HERE AND
DON'T MAKE
A NOISE,
NO MATTER
WHAT.

KOKU
(NOD)
コク

SU
(FWISH)
スッ

SUUU
スゥー

うるっ…
URU (SOB)

YOU SHOULDN'T GET SEPARATED FROM US, YOU KNOW.

I...

I'M SORRY!

GABA (GLOMP)

AS LONG AS YOU UNDERSTAND.

OH, THERE YOU ARE.

THE GHOST? OH, YOU MEAN THE STUDENT WHO STAYED BEHIND. I JUST SAW HIM OFF.

BUT YOU SAID I SHOULD STAY QUIET...

MEGU-NEE! WHERE WERE YOU!? WHAT ABOUT THE GHOST?

OH, YOU'RE ALL TOGETHER.

HYOKO (PEEK)

WELL, IF YOU THREE ARE AROUND, IT'S HARD TO EXPLAIN THINGS WHEN I HAVE TO SCOLD SOMEONE.

THAT'S SO MEAN!

NEXT YEAR...

YES, THAT'S A PROMISE.

PROM-ISE!

SU (REACH)

IT WAS FUN! LET'S DO IT AGAIN NEXT YEAR!

SO, DID YOU ENJOY THE TEST OF COURAGE?

BAG: BALLOONS 20x INFLATION

ZAAAAA
(FSSSHHH)

KACHI
(TICK)

KOCHI
(TICK)

THIS WILL
PROBABLY
BE MY
WILL.

KURUMI-CHAN, IT'S RAINING.

YEAH. ALL THE SPORTS TEAMS ARE RUNNING TO GET OUT OF THE RAIN.

PARA
ぱ
ら

PARA
(PATTER)
ぱ
ら

REALLY?

HEY! DON'T PLAY WITH IT!

BA (YANK)

AWW!

WHAT ARE YOU, A GRADE SCHOOLER?

LOOK AT THE JIGGLE!

RII-SAN'S BRA. ←

SIGN: SCHOOL MOTTO

KIIN (BING)

KOON (BONG)

It's time for lunch. Let's all get proper nutrition for the sake of our afternoon classes.

校訓

HURRY UP, OR THEY'LL ALL GET WET.

OKAY!

PATA (PATTER)

PATA

LET'S EAT.

THAT'S BECAUSE THE POWER'S OUT IN THE ENTIRE SCHOOL.

BORI
BORI

HMM. THEY'RE SO DRY.

PORI (CRUNCH)

MUSHA (CHOMP)

I LIKE IT WHEN THE POWER'S OUT.

IT'S KINDA EXCITING.

MUSHA

AAAH!

YOU WON'T GET ANY HOT WATER.

THE HEATER FOR OUR SHOWER IS ELECTRIC, YOU KNOW.

HUH?

GAAN (SHOCK)

YOU OKAY?

BA (WHOOSH)

......

WE'RE CAMPING!

YOU KNOW, UMM, YOU GO CAMPING ON FIELD TRIPS, RIGHT? WE'RE THE SCHOOL LIVING CLUB, SO WE'RE CAMPING AT SCHOOL!

CAMPING?

THERE SHOULD BE ONE IN THE CLUBROOM. IT SHOULD FIT THE THREE OF US.

HEY! BUT ME, ME!

CAMPING, HUH? I WONDER IF WE HAVE A TENT.

YES. THAT WORKS, DOESN'T IT?

I GET IT. WHEN YOU'RE CAMPING, YOU DON'T HAVE STUFF LIKE ELECTRICITY.

あ PAA (SHINE)

SORRY. I DIDN'T MEAN IT LIKE THAT.

!

I-IT'S OKAY! IF WE ALL SQUEEZE IN, WE CAN FIT YOU, MEGU-NEE!

I'M JUST JOKING. I HAVE ROUNDS TO MAKE.

THANKS FOR ALWAYS DOING THAT, MEGU-NEE!

THANKS, MEGU-NEE!

HONESTLY!

IT'S SAKURA-SENSEI, NOT MEGU-NEE.

HEY, WHAT SHOULD WE TALK ABOUT?

THIS IS TOTALLY THE RIGHT ATMO-SPHERE!

DID YOU KNOW? ON RAINY DAYS LIKE TODAY...

NO WAY!

WHA? IT DOES FEEL RIGHT, BUT STILL...

WE SHOULD TELL GHOST STORIES.

Owww!

BITAAN (THWACK)

CHOP!

FU FU...

OH, I JUST THOUGHT OF SOMETHING REALLY SCARY...

LET'S TALK ABOUT SOMETHING CHEERFUL! LIKE LOVE!

I CAN SEE THAT. SHE'S A GOOD TEACHER.

YEAH, SHE IS. AND WE WOULDN'T HAVE THIS CLUB WITHOUT HER EITHER.

...I GOT A BIT SAD.

GYU‼... (SQUEEZE)

WHEN I THOUGHT ABOUT THAT...

AND SOMETIMES SHE MESSES UP WRITING ON THE BLACKBOARD.

PFFT!

AND SHE GIVES A LOT OF HOMEWORK.

YEAH. SHE'S REALLY NICE... THOUGH I GET SLEEPY IN HER CLASS.

GABA
(FLUMP)

PIKU
(TWITCH)

KOTSU
(CLACK)

KOTSU

AHHH!

IT'S
MEGU-
NEE!

HUH?

FUTA
(PANIC)

ATA
(PANIC)

SU
(STEP)

GACHA
(CLATTER)

PA
(SHINE)

HELLO?
ARE THERE
ANY BAD
GIRLS HERE
WHO ARE
STAYING UP
TOO LATE?

......

... もぞっ... MOZO (SNUGGLE)

THERE AREN'T ANY, ARE THERE? GOOD NIGHT, THEN.

IT'S OKAY NOW.

SO (PEEK)

BWA!

ぱたん PATAN (SHUT)

HA-HA.

PU (PFFT)

YOU CAN'T STOP THE FLOW OF TIME.

IF ONE DAY THOSE THREE...

...CAN MAKE IT OUT OF THIS SCHOOL SMILING...

...I DON'T CARE WHAT HAPPENS TO ME TO MAKE THAT HAPPEN.

SCHOOL-LIVE!

SO (BRUSH)

YOU KNOW...

...I DECIDED THIS WITH YUURI-CHAN.

HIKKU (SOB)

HIKKU

WITH RII-SAN?

YES. IT'S GOING TO BE A LOT OF FUN.

IT COULDN'T POSSIBLY... BE FUN...

WE'RE STARTING A CLUB! ALL OF US, TOGETHER!

(GUSUN) (SNIFFLE)

...CLUB...?

A...

MMPH...

むく
MUKU
(RISE)

OH...

HMM?
THE STAFF
ROOM,
MAYBE?

WHERE'S
MEGU-NEE?

WHAT
IS IT?

GII
(CREAK)

ぶるっ
BURU
(SHAKE)

UMM.

GOTTA PEE.

もじ MOJI

もじ MOJI (FIDGET)

ARE YOU SLEEP-WALKING?

キュッ KYU (TUG)

IT'S OKAY. I CAN GO BY MYSELF.

OKAY. JUST WAIT A MINUTE.

YOU'RE BEING OVERPRO-TECTIVE!

SHUT UP! THOSE ARE THE RULES.

ガタ GATA (CLATTER)

カチッ KACHI (CLICK)

ズ ZU (SLIDE)

GOOD JOB.

BISHI
(FWIP)
ビシッ

RULE NUMBER THREE. YOU MUST AVOID ACTING ALONE AT NIGHT AND ALWAYS TRAVEL IN NUMBERS!

SCHOOL LIVING CLUB RULE NUMBER THREE!

ばん
BAN
(SHOVE)

RII-SAN, MORNING!

OUR ADVISOR WILL GET INTO TROUBLE IF WE WANDER AROUND ALONE IN THE MIDDLE OF THE NIGHT.

DON'T ACT LIKE YOU HAVE NOTHING TO DO WITH THIS!

IT MUST BE REALLY ROUGH FOR MEGU-NEE.

114

...JUST KIDDING.

I LIKE SCHOOL AT NIGHT.

PATAN (SHUT)

IT'S SUPER QUIET, SO YOU CAN'T HEAR ANYTHING.

IT'S ALMOST LIKE THERE'S NO ONE ELSE IN THE WHOLE WORLD AND WE'RE ALL ALONE.

TEKU (TROT)

TEKU

IT'S RAINING AGAIN.

OH.

ZAAAAAAAA (FSSSHHH)

女子トイレ

!

IT'S PROBABLY A DELINQUENT.

...HEY, SOME-ONE'S COMING.

SASA (FWISH)

GYU (GRIP)

JUST BE QUIET AND DON'T MEET THEIR EYES.

WH-WHAT SHOULD WE DO?

O-OKAY.

THAT WAS SCARY!

FUUU (SIIIGH)

OH, BUT HE MIGHT, SINCE IT'S A BAD KID.

BIKU (FLINCH)

I'LL GO GET SOMEONE. YOU WAIT HERE.

THE BAD KID WON'T COME INTO THE BATHROOM, RIGHT?

HETOOO (SLUMP)

HUH? THAT'S DANGEROUS.

IT'S OKAY! I CAN TAKE CARE OF A DELINQUENT WITH ONE SWING!

...OKAY, I GET IT. JUST LOCK THE DOOR FOR NOW.

O-OKAY.

LIKE THE KIND OF PERSON WHO'D BRING HOME A PUPPY? I MEAN, IT IS RAINING.

WHAT DO YOU MEAN A GOOD BAD KID?

I MEAN THAT'S DANGEROUS FOR THE BAD KID! IT MIGHT BE A GOOD BAD KID!

DEEEEN (TADAA)

.......HMM.

ZUKIN (THROB)

IT'LL BE FINE. I'LL BE RIGHT BACK, SO DON'T MOVE.

PON (PAT)

—OKAY...

I'LL BE RIGHT BACK.

IT'S OKAY.

OH, UH, NOTHING.

HMM?

HUH?

SU
(BREATHE)

DON'T WORRY ABOUT IT!

KURUMI-CHAN, BE REALLY, REALLY CAREFUL!

ZAWA (CHILL)

PARA (PATTER)

PARA

YEAH. ALL THE SPORTS TEAMS ARE RUNNING TO GET OUT OF THE RAIN.

POCHAN (DROP)

SO THIS IS WHAT SHE MEANT BY GETTING OUT OF THE RAIN!?

DAMMIT!

YUKI TAKEYA-SAN.

SOOO (PEEK)

SHE'S REALLY TAKING A LONG TIME...

HMM...

WHAT ARE YOU DOING? YOU'RE NOT SUPPOSED TO GO OUTSIDE ALONE.

MEGU-NEE!

B-BUT KURUMI-CHAN...

EBISUZAWA-SAN?

VERY WELL. I'LL GO FIND HER.

O-OKAY.

SA (FWISH)

...OKAY LIKE THIS?

AM I...

......UM.

GYU (TUG)

I'M NOT...

WHAT?

...WEIGHING EVERYONE DOWN, AM I?

DOTE (THUD)

OUT OF MY WAY!!

GESU (THUNK)

BA (WHOOSH)

ARGH!

GUOOO (GRAAAH)

GII (CREAK)

HFF...

HFF...

GAN (THWACK)

GOSU (THWACK)

BUO

BUN (SWING)

It's time
to head
home.

グッ
GU
(PRESS)

シュウウウ
SHUUUUU
(FSSSHHH)

RII-
SAN
!?

KURUMI!

プシュウウウウウウ
PUSHUUUU
(FSSSHHH)

グシャ
GSHK

ウ
ウ
ウ

HFF...

I TURNED
ON THE
ANNOUNCEMENT
ON THE
SECOND
FLOOR. LOOKS
LIKE IT'S
ATTRACTING
THEM.

ズズズズ
GUOOO

ゴスッ
GOSU
(THUD)

シュウウウウザザザ
SHUUUUU

OH...

ふ
FUUU
(SIGH)

SHE'S WAITING IN THE BATHROOM.

HUP.

WHERE'S YUKI-CHAN?

PHEW.

HEY, YUKI.

KON (KNOCK) KON

GEEZ, IF WE DON'T HURRY UP, SHE'LL...

MEGU-NEE?

OH, BUT WHAT ABOUT MEGU-NEE?

OH, SORRY.

SHE WENT TO GO LOOK FOR YOU BECAUSE YOU WERE TAKING SO LONG.

IF WE DON'T HURRY UP...THEN WHAT...?

...HUH?

IF WE DON'T HURRY UP...

HUH?

IT'S SOMETHING IMPORTANT.

SOMETHING SUPER IMPORTANT...

JUST NOW...

WHAT WAS THAT?

WHAT WAS IT...?

KYU
(SQUEAK)

KYU

KYU

PITA
(STOP)

UHHH...

SIGNS: STUDENT COUNCIL, SCHOOL LIVING CLUB

OH?

HENA
(SLUMP)

HENAA

I CAN'T ANYMORE!

OH? WHAT'S WRONG?

UJI
(SWAY)

KURUMI-CHAN'S STRONG TOO.

AND RII-SAN'S SMART.

YOU'RE REALLY STRONG, MEGU-NEE.

WELL, I WAS WONDERING IF I'M REALLY OKAY LIKE THIS.

BEING A TEACHER ACTUALLY INVOLVES A LOT OF PHYSICAL LABOR.

...THAT DOESN'T REALLY MAKE ME FEEL ANY BETTER.

YOUR SMILE?

NIKO (SMILE)

YOU HAVE YOUR OWN GOOD QUALITIES, YOU KNOW.

THERE WE GO.

LIKE WHAT?

REALLY?

IT'S NOT LIKE THAT.

YES.

SMILING CHEERS PEOPLE UP.

DOYOOON (GLOOM)

IT WOULD BE HORRIBLE IF EVERYONE WAS ALWAYS GLOOMY, WOULDN'T IT?

UGH. YEAH, IT WOULD...

PACHI
(BLINK)

—YUKI-
CHAN.

YUKI...!

MUKURI
(RISE)

OH,
MORNING!

YOU WOULDN'T WAKE UP.

WA (CLAMOR)

OH, GOOD!

WH- WHAT'S WRONG?

WHERE'S MEGU- NEE?

KYORO (GLANCE)

KYORO

NOB!!! (STREEETCH)

OH...

OH!

YUKI- CHAN, MEGU- NEE'S...

MEGU-NEE, MORNING!

HEY, IS THERE ANYTHING TO EAT?

I'M REALLY HUNGRY.

OF COURSE. DO YOU WANT SOME UDON?

YEAH, I LOVE UDON!

もぞっ
MOZO
(SLIDE)

SMILING CHEERS PEOPLE UP.

BUT BE SURE NOT TO EAT TOO MUCH.

OKAY!

GOKUN (GULP)

2 - 5

YOU'VE BEEN SICK, SO MAKE SURE YOU CHEW EVERYTHING THOROUGHLY.

YOU EAT TOO FAST!

I DID CHEW EVERYTHING!

HMPH.

MORE!

DEN (TADAA)

NO. THERE ISN'T ANY LEFT AT THE SCHOOL STORE.

WE'LL HAVE TO GO OUTSIDE.

ANOTHER TEST OF COURAGE?

ちゅるっ
CHURU (SLURP)

THERE ISN'T ANY MORE. WE HAVE TO GO GET SOME.

SORRY.

CHIRA (GLANCE)

ちら
っ

GARA
(SLIDE)

OKAY!

YOU'RE RIGHT. CAN YOU GO ASK HER?

THEN WE'LL HAVE TO ASK MEGU-NEE FOR PERMIS-SION!

モグ (MUNCH) MOGU

CHARIN
(JINGLE)

WE'RE NOT JUST RUNNING OUT OF UDON.

WE HAVE TO GO EVENTUALLY.

THANKS FOR THE FOOD.

GATA
(CLATTER)

OUTSIDE...? WHAT ARE YOU GONNA DO IF MEGU-NEE SAYS OKAY?

JURU
(SLURP)

WELL, I GUESS.

GEPU
(URP)

I'M BACK!

SHE DOES HAVE TO DEAL WITH STAFF MEETINGS AND STUFF, AFTER ALL.

NAH.

SHE'S MAKING SUCH A BIG DEAL OF IT.

SHE SAID IT'S OKAY, BUT WE HAVE TO TURN IN A REQUEST IN WRITING.

HOW DID IT GO?

SO WHAT ARE WE GONNA DO TODAY?

THAT'S TRUE.

SO WE SEND THEM FROM THE SCHOOL.

HUH? LETTERS? BUT THE POST OFFICE IS OUTSIDE.

WHY DON'T WE WRITE LETTERS?

KURUPPOO (COOO)
クルッ、ポー

IF WE'RE WRITING LETTERS, THEN WE NEED CARRIER PIGEONS!

FOR LETTERS, WE HAVE THESE!

YEAH, YEAH.

THEN WE CATCH ONE!

JAAAAN (TADAAA)
じゃーん

BISHI (FWISH)
ビシッ

GOSO (RUMMAGE)
ゴソ

GOSO
ゴソ

BAG: BALLOON 20x INFLATION

WE DON'T HAVE ANY CARRIER PIGEONS.

SHIRA (STARE)
しらっ

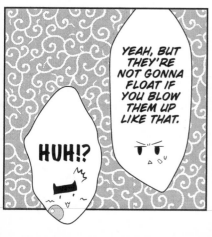

YEAH, BUT THEY'RE NOT GONNA FLOAT IF YOU BLOW THEM UP LIKE THAT.

HUH!?

YEAH, FROM THE TEST OF COURAGE.

OH, THOSE ARE FROM BEFORE.

PUUUU (BLOOOW)
プーーーーっ

OH YEAH!

THEN I'LL GO GET IT.

THERE MIGHT BE SOME HELIUM IN THE SCIENCE ROOM.

GATA (CLATTER)

HOW ABOUT YOU WRITE THE LETTERS?

ME TOO...

I'M GONNA WRITE! IT'S GONNA BE AMAZING!

OKAY!

BOOK: ATLAS

WHAT'S THAT?

PERA (FLIP)

HMM.

THAT'S WHAT IT SAYS.

THIS IS WHERE WE ARE.

E 139.645
N 25 418

IT'S JUST KINDA EMBAR-RASSING TO WRITE IT NOW. AND MY HAND-WRITING'S SO MESSY...

WHAT'S WRONG?

HMMM ...

KESHI (RUB)

けし
け し
KESHI

WHAT WOULD YOU THINK IF YOU PICKED UP A BALLOON FROM THE SIDE OF THE ROAD AND THERE WAS A LETTER ATTACHED TO IT?

RIGHT?

NAH. I'D JUST BE REALLY HAPPY TO GET A LETTER!

WOULD YOU THINK, "THIS PERSON HAS SLOPPY HANDWRITING"?

I'D BE SURPRISED! AND HAPPY!

I'M BACK!

GARA (RATTLE)

GARA

OH!

FUYO
ふよ

FUYO
(FLOAT)
ふよ

SHUUU
(FSSHH)
シュ

SOOO
(SLOWLY)
ス

KURUPPOO
(COOO)
クルッポ

COO?

POSU
(THUMP)

COO....

BASA

BASA
(FLAP)

BASSA

BASSA
(FLAP)

DEN (TADAA)

IT'S TIME.

ALL RIGHT!

HER. HATOKO HATONISHIKI-CHAN.

WAIT A MINUTE. WHO ARE YOU CALLING HATOKO-CHAN?

YOU WORK HARD TOO, HATOKO-CHAN.

OKAY!

HOW ABOUT WE SPLIT THE DIFFERENCE AND CALL IT ARNAUD HATONISHIKI?

AWWW, BUT I WANNA NAME HER TOO!

IT'S NOT HATOKO-CHAN! IT'S ARNAUD.

KURUPPOO
(COO)

BASA
(FLAP)

BASA

ALL RIGHT! FLY FOR US, ARNAUD HATONISHIKI!

MAYBE SHE'LL FLY ALL THE WAY TO AMERICA.

OFFICIALLY NAMED "ARNAUD HATO-NISHIKI."

THAT KINDA MAKES YOU SOUND HALF FOREIGN.

READY?

OKAY, ON THE COUNT OF THREE!

THREE!

PA
(FWIP)

TWO.

ONE.

WE WILL.

I WONDER IF THEY'LL MAKE IT. I WONDER IF WE'LL GET A RESPONSE.

IF WE DON'T, WE CAN JUST SEND OUT SOME MORE.

YOU'RE REALLY SMART, KURUMI-CHAN!

YEAH!

SCHOOL-LIVE!

Megurigaoka Academy Private High School

~~2012~~ A.D.

Campus Information

Headmaster's Greeting

Our school's educational philosophy: "Independence and Autonomy."

The three years of high school are an invaluable time for young people flying toward the future. The entire meaning of school life is to prepare them for the adult society that awaits them, to give them all manner of different experiences, and to give them the power to carry on when they occasionally misstep. No matter how amazing their knowledge and skills may be, such treasures will remain unused without the will to wield them.

The founding principle of our school was "Independence and Autonomy," and we seek to provide an education that focuses the school, the family, and the student as one on fostering the student's ability to act in accordance with their own abilities.

A School that Is a Village

In order to uphold the principle of independence and autonomy, we at the academy view the school as a miniature version of society at large and have prepared various facilities to allow the students to gain a wide variety of experiences.

Megurigaoka Academy is a village, and as residents of the village, the students can try their hands at various jobs, always with the goal of becoming self-sufficient.

Education Sought After for the New Era

The importance of the spirit of independence and autonomy will never change, no matter what age we are in, but the desired focus of an education changes with the times. In these modern times during which the all-importance of academic credentials and the idea of lifetime employment have gone by the wayside, the ability to better oneself through an individualized plan, or perhaps the power to survive through raising others up, has become essential.

In order to give everyone the power to rise above the stormy seas of society, Megurigaoka Academy strives to provide a practical education.

Our entire staff awaits the enrollment of everyone who has read this pamphlet.

Megurigaoka Academy Headmaster
Jouji Andou

The History of the Institution

Surrounded by the history of Megurigaoka City.

The city of Megurigaoka in S Prefecture was long known as Dando, and people were quite close to the bounty of nature here. The city of Dando was known for its plentiful folklore, and the city is mentioned in books such as the classic *Snake Gods of the Impure Land* and the more modern *Devilish Thinking*. The city also kept a strong naval force, and H-shi, a professor of archaeology at K University, has compared the folklore of Dando to that of the West Indies and pointed out the possibility of a cultural exchange between the two places.

After the heartbreaking events of 1968, the worries of a further decline in population led the city of Dando to apply for a city development project. In 1979, the city changed its name to Megurigaoka and began to encourage corporations and local industries to set up business in the area, which has been the cornerstone of the community's current prosperity.

Megurigaoka, the name of both the city and the school, comes from the local rolling countryside and the desire to attain the cultural prosperity of ancient Rome brought by the people who visited the seven hills of Rome.

~721	The Ancient Records of Hajima were established around this time. The name Dando begins to be seen.
1889	The city of Dando is established. The city prospers through fishing and its navy.
1968	Half of the population of Dando is wiped out this year. Later on, this becomes known as Dando's nighttime.
1970	Dando applies for a city development project. The public is asked for ideas for a new city name.
1979	Dando's city development project is approved. The same year, the city's name is changed to Megurigaoka. Other proposed names included Ryuusei. (Dando's dawn.)
1984	This year, Dando's population rises to its highest since 1968. (Dando's morning.)
1987	Megurigaoka Academy Private High School is established.
1997	Tenth anniversary of Megurigaoka Academy Private High School.
2007	Twentieth anniversary of Megurigaoka Academy Private High School.

Tour of the Facility

At our school, which strives to function as a self-sufficient village, we have various facilities in the building that are necessary to allow the students to experience different aspects of living in society.

Vegetable Gardens

The heart of independence and autonomy begins with food. Knowing this, our school is in the unique position of having vegetable gardens on the roof and in two other locations on campus, as well as keeping contract farms off campus.

These gardens are mostly tended to and harvested by students taking extracurricular courses or in the gardening club. The harvested foodstuffs are then cooked and fed to the students, while some portion is sold directly to the community under the popular Megurigaoka vegetables brand.

The vegetable gardens being bathed in sunlight.

Water Purification System

Just as important to life as food is water. Our school draws water from the ground and the Kuchina River and passes it through our very own purification system to be used for such things as drinking or to fill the pool.

The purification system is powered by in-house generators, so the entire region could use the school as a base in case of a disaster.

Power Generators

Ranking alongside food and water in importance to modern society is power. At our school, the building is powered by both solar panels on the roof and hydroelectric turbines in the Kuchina River.

The distribution of this energy is decided by the student council. The extra power is sold back to the city, and this money, along with the savings on water rates because of the water purification system, is included in the budget for the Ryuusei Festival to teach the students the importance of saving energy even in school.

Computer Labs

In the modern age of Internet society, computers are not just tools for learning, but also great weapons, as well as the way to protect against such attacks. Our school has been using computers in learning since before the Internet existed, and we have been on the leading edge of computer education right up to the current day.

In our state-of-the-art computer labs, students learn not just the basics of how to use a computer, but also Internet literacy and security.

Student Kitchens

The majority of the vegetables from the school gardens are cooked in the student kitchens and then used in student meals.

To aid in this, the student kitchens are large, efficient, and outfitted with the latest equipment, matching the scope of the gardens.

In particular, all of the kitchens in the school are put to work for the Kyuusei Festival.

Emergency Food Stores

A portion of the produce from the gardens is preserved in the emergency food stores in the basement. The food in the stores runs from rice and wheat to our own special pickled vegetables. The gardening club's signature ten-year pickled plums are only brought out for special events and celebrations.

The school store, stocked with an abundance of goods.

Library

In the spirit of independence and autonomy, the management of the collection in the school's library is mostly left to the students (the library committee).

In addition to the various books needed for academic study, there is a system to add new books according to student polls and requests. The wide variety of texts, including manga and other recreational works, is quite popular.

School Store and Gardening Club

In addition to items for every area of study, the school store sells goods made by the students themselves in their club activities, starting with the uniforms made by the handicrafts club, and a portion of the proceeds from these goods is returned to the clubs as part of their budgets. The gardening club's prize vegetables are used as part of the established school lunches.

The library's collection runs from books necessary for learning to material for fun and practical use.

At Megurigaoka Academy, we put our efforts into a quality academic education as well as various extracurricular courses to provide experiences that teach the spirit of independence and autonomy.

Foreign Language Learning

Our school encourages students to succeed across national borders, so we offer classes in English and ten other languages, including French and Chinese, taught by native speakers that we have invited to our school.

Extracurricular Courses

At our school, we offer courses in all manner of subjects, not just those restricted to the classroom, and every year countless students make use of these courses.

We bring in experts from various fields to offer courses such as the robot course, where students build a hobby robot over the course of a year, or the anime course, where students produce a completed short-form anime. The most popular course, the natural experiences course, in which students catch fish in the nearby Kuchina River and cook them, attracts countless students every year.

Club Activities

Club activities at our school strive to promote exchange with the community. The sports teams as well as the cultural clubs are quite close with local residents, thanks to things such as the charity concerts put on by the guitar club and the brass band, and the sale of the gardening club's vegetables.

The Ryuusei Festival

The cultural festival, held every year in October, is the prime occasion for students to show the spirit of independence and autonomy, as well as the top reason students give for choosing our school.

The name of the Ryuusei Festival comes from the legend of a saint who defeated an evil dragon, and the story is performed by the drama club as the *Ryuusei Drama*. Every year the *Ryuusei Drama*, which interprets the legend in various ways, receives much praise from the community.

The Megurigaoka Academy School Song

Lyrics: Unknown (Old Folk Song)
Adaptation of Lyrics: Takashi Yushimoto
Song: Akira Shirai

First among the seven hills
is the saint whose blade glitters like the heavens.
Roiling in the Kuchina River
is the poison breath of the great nine-headed serpent.

Seven days and seven nights of fighting.
What fell from the heavens were tears of blood,
which soaked deep into the ground.
The remains of the fires were the true horror.

The sun travels over the seven hills.
Now the saint is no longer here,
but our incomparable saint's descendants
wield his sword in their hearts.

Hold courage fast in your heart.
Go, people of Megurigaoka.

Megurigaoka Academy Private High School

~~20XX~~ A.D.

Campus Information

Text: Norimitsu Kaihou
Editorial Assistance: Ryou Morise (Chronocraft)
Design: Shougo Iwahori (a-ism design)

Girls having a fun little tea party in their classroom while you can see the ruined city outside the window.

This is the sight that came to mind while I was chatting at dinner with my usual group of buddies.

Someone said that it was an interesting idea, and then I met Sadoru Chiba-san, who turned my hazy idea into something that made me go, "This! It has to be this!" And with so many connections just like that, and the help of so many people I couldn't name them all, this book came into being.

There really are so many people that I want to thank, but first my gratitude goes to the pioneers.

To Mary Shelley, Richard Matheson, George Romero, Tom Savini, and Brian Yuzna.

And to you, the person who picked up this book.

Thank you.

Norimitsu Kaihō

Next time
they're at a
shopping mall.
A mall!!

Translation Notes

Common Honorifics:

no honorific: Indicates familiarity or closeness; if used without permission or reason, addressing someone in this manner would constitute an insult.

-san: The Japanese equivalent of Mr./Mrs./Miss. If a situation calls for politeness, this is the fail-safe honorific.

-chan: An affectionate honorific indicating familiarity used mostly in reference to girls; also used in reference to cute persons or animals of either gender.

-senpai: A suffix used to address upperclassmen or more experienced coworkers.

-sensei: A respectful term for teachers, artists, or high-level professionals.

-nee: Honorific derived from onee-san/sama ("big sister"). -nee when used alone after a name can mean closeness.

Page 58

Umakabo is a parody of *Umaibo*, a popular stick-shaped snack.

Page 74

All the manga titles on the shelf are parodies of other *Manga Time Kirara* titles, which is where *School-Live!* is being serialized.

Page 158

Hatoko Hatonishiki: Yuki is giving the pigeon the most straightforward name with *Hato* meaning pigeon and *nishiki* meaning beautiful.

SCHOOL-LIVE! ❶

Loot Crate
Exclusive
Edition

SADORU CHIBA
NORIMITSU KAIHOU
(NITROPLUS)

Translation: Leighann Harvey

Lettering: Alexis Eckerman

GAKKOU GURASHI! Loot Crate Exclusive Edition Vol. 1
©Nitroplus / Norimitsu Kaihou, Sadoru Chiba, Houbunsha. All rights reserved. First published in Japan in 2012 by HOUBUNSHA CO., LTD., Tokyo. English translation rights in United States, Canada, and United Kingdom arranged with HOUBUNSHA CO., LTD through Tuttle-Mori Agency, Inc., Tokyo.

English translation © 2015 by Yen Press, LLC

Yen Press
1290 Avenue of the Americas
New York, NY 10104

Visit us at yenpress.com
facebook.com/yenpress
twitter.com/yenpress
yenpress.tumblr.com
instagram.com/yenpress

First Loot Crate Exclusive Edition: April 2017
Originally published in paperback in November 2015 by Yen Press.

Yen Press is an imprint of Yen Press, LLC.
The Yen Press name and logo are trademarks of Yen Press, LLC.

The publisher is not responsible for websites (or their content) that are not owned by the publisher.

ISBN: 978-0-316-47278-4

10 9 8 7 6 5 4 3 2 1

BVG

Printed in the United States of America